Corrie's Curling Capers

ILLUSTRATED BY
TONY van BREUGEL

WRITTEN BY
ALISON PAGE

For Dougie

With fond childhood memories of Mum's Canadian roots and Dad's curling boots.

In loving memory of Corrie, a very precious wee Westie.

Other titles in the Corrie's Capers series:
The Westie Fest
The Tattoo Toorie

First published in Scotland in 2020

ISBN 9781999926526

Text copyright © Alison Page
Illustrations copyright © Tony van Breugel

What is Corrie up to?

The document held by the character reads:

Caledonian Canine Curling Club

Corrie
The Westie Fest Champion
is invited to open
the CCCC Bonspiel.

As our guest of honour
you are requested
to deliver the first stone
up the ice.

She is practising her sweeping strokes!
The Caledonian Canine Curling Club has invited her
to open their bonspiel.

Corrie has never played curling before,
but she always enjoys watching the Winter Olympics on television.

There's no ice rink on Arran,
so Corrie slides up and down the hall floor instead.
Wheeeeeee! What fun!

Corrie remembers that
there are some
old curling stones
sitting at Papa's doorstep.

She decides to go
and ask him about them.

Papa digs out the family
photograph albums
from the kist.

They coorie in by the fire and pore over the old photos.

Aha!
Here's the photo he's looking for.

During bitterly cold winters, the ice was so thick on the pond the islanders were able to play curling on it.

Papa's family were keen curlers and played for the Lamlash team in the Challenge Medal.

The old curling stones at the front door of Bluebell Cottage belonged to them.

Papa tells Corrie that two hundred years ago
times were very hard. Many families had to leave their homes.
Papa's relatives left Arran in 1829 to start a new life in Canada.

Before she left Arran, Anabella (Papa's *great, great, great, great* grandmother) was given a small granite pebble by her grandfather. It was from Ailsa Craig, which means 'Fairy Rock' in Gaelic.

If Anabella ever felt worried, all she had to do was hold this polished pebble in her paw to help her remember happy days at home on Arran.

There was only space on board for tools
and a few personal belongings. Curling stones were far too heavy
to carry and were left behind at the old croft.

There were no aeroplanes in those days.
You had to take a very long boat journey across dangerous seas.

Soon after they left Scotland, there was a big storm.
The brig heaved and rolled. Even the sailors felt terribly seasick.

Anabella
closed her eyes
and squeezed
the pebble tightly
in her paw.

Her grandfather was
right – thinking of home
did help her feel better.

The sea became calm
and they continued on their long voyage to Canada.

Corrie still has cousins living in Canada. Papa tells her that they play in the Canadian curling team!

Corrie really wants to meet them. It sounds like the perfect time to invite them for a family reunion!

The Scottish and Canadian clans gather together in Glasgow.

Corrie's cousins enjoy a tour of the city.

Glasgow City Chambers

House for an Art Lover

Kibble Palace

Kelvingrove Art Gallery and Museum

Gallery of Modern Art

Glasgow Cathedral

The Mitchell Library

Òran Mór

Kelvinbridge

Next, they head to the ice rink where Corrie is given her first curling lesson.

Oo-er... She's a wee bitty wibbly wobbly. Corrie needs lots more practice or she might topple over when she opens the bonspiel!

Afterwards, there's even more excitement as they get ready to board The Waverley Paddle Steamer at Pacific Quay for a sail 'doon the watter' to Arran via Ailsa Craig.

The captain explains that Ailsa Craig sits in the middle of the Firth of Clyde and was once the top of a volcano!

Only birds live on the island now, but the best curling stones in the world are still made with granite taken from the quarry on Ailsa Craig.

How *amazing* would it be to play with those curling stones!

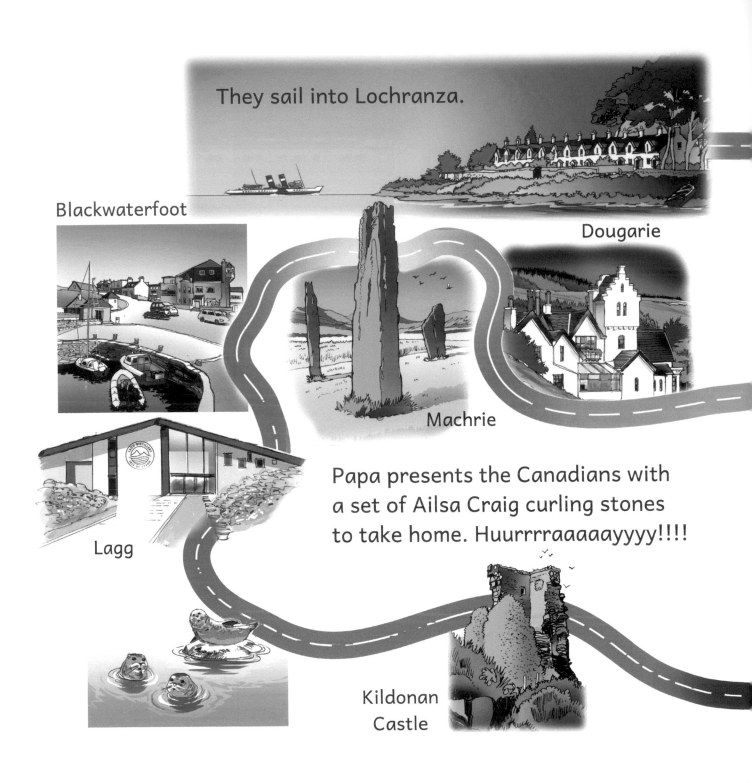

They sail into Lochranza.

Blackwaterfoot

Dougarie

Machrie

Papa presents the Canadians with
a set of Ailsa Craig curling stones
to take home. Huurrrraaaaayyyy!!!!

Lagg

Kildonan
Castle

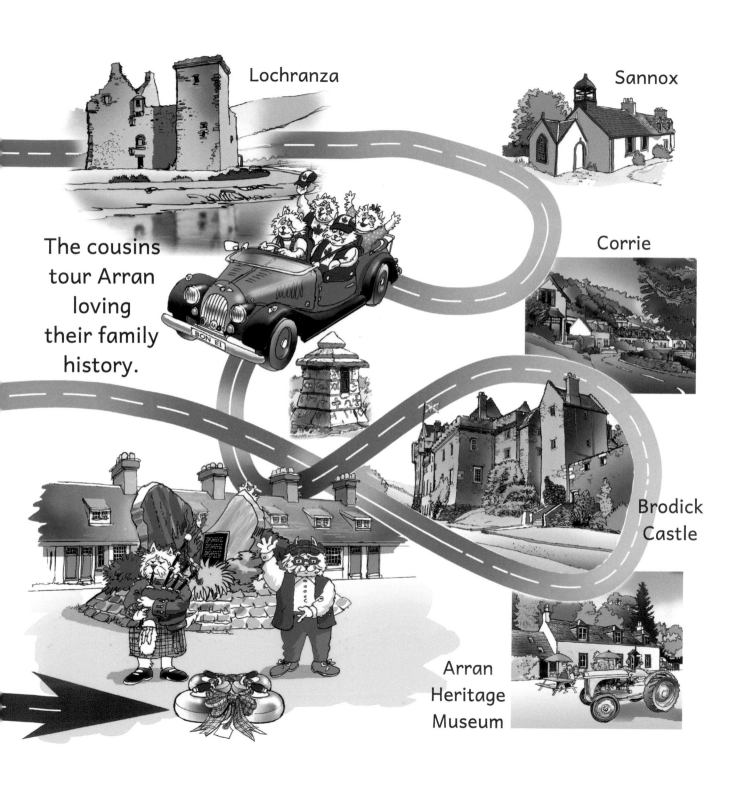

Lochranza

Sannox

Corrie

The cousins tour Arran loving their family history.

Brodick Castle

Arran Heritage Museum

They finish off the day with a fantastic party in the village hall.

Gran Flora's Knit 'n' Natter group swap their knitting needles for baking bowls, pots and pans. What a scrumptious feast!

The ceilidh is in full swing.

Everyone is on the dance floor, g'ien it laldy, when disaster strikes!

Corrie and Archie spin round and round so fast,
they lose their grip and part company!

Corrie lands on her bahookie and everyone gasps as Archie falls
backwards into the buffet table sending everything flying.

The shocked silence quickly turns into howls of laughter as Corrie and her cousins slide up and down the slippery floor sweeping up the mess.

Corrie's curling lessons have certainly come in very handy!

They all join paws to sing Auld Lang Syne to end a very special family reunion.

As her cousins are leaving, Dugald gives Corrie a mysterious-looking parcel.

'This has been in our family for years,' he says. 'It came from Scotland originally and is very special. We'd really like you to have it.'

Corrie carefully unwraps the package and finds a polished pebble inside.

Wow! Can this possibly be the Fairy Rock Papa had talked about?

It's the day of the Caledonian Canine Curling Club bonspiel.
Hmm... Do you think Corrie might wibble-wobble?
Has she practised enough?

Corrie looks cool and calm as she confidently glides out over the ice.

Can you guess what Corrie has tucked in her pocket?

It's Anabella's pebble from Ailsa Craig, of course!

Papa's family won the Challenge Medal.
Your challenge is to spot 10 differences.

Glossary

Auld Lang Syne	A song about old memories and days gone by. Traditionally used to bring in the New Year, it is also sung as a farewell or ending to other social occasions
bahookie	Backside or bottom
bonspiel	A large scale match or contest in curling
brig	A sailing vessel with two square-rigged masts popular in the 18th century
ceilidh	A social event with Scottish music and dancing
coorie in	Cuddle/Snuggle in
doon the watter	A sail down the river Clyde
g'ien it laldy	Giving your all/doing something exuberantly
kist	Chest

Alison's Acknowledgements

Dear John and Alexander,
Thank you for your love and patience throughout the many stages of this most enjoyable Corrie's Capers journey.

With very special thanks to:
Tony van Breugel for illustrating book 3, introducing his Dutch wit, wonderfully unique artistic flair and creative interpretation for Corrie and her Curling Capers.
Judith Paskin for offering such solid editorial guidance, friendship and support.
June Caldwell for her professionalism, resilience and tenacity with typography and layout.
Richard Trewby for his eagle eye proof reading.
Graham Chappell for his professional printing services through Arran Graphics.

Thanks also to:
Lynne Macvicar for sharing the McKillop family history dating back to the 1800s.
Stuart Gough and John Lauder for their assistance in finding extracts relating to curling from the Social History Archives at the Isle of Arran Heritage Museum.
Holywood Ladies (Dumfries) and Mid Calder Curling Club for such fun playing curling with them so many years ago.

Finally, thank YOU for buying this book.
Profits are donated to the Scottish based charity Mary's Meals **www.marysmeals.org.uk**
Find out more about Corrie at **www.westie.scot**